MW00795120

An Interesting
Trip

by Jamie Margaret
illustrated by Richard Hoit

SCHOOL PUBLISHERS

3 ©Barclay Gibson/TexasEscapes.com; 8 ©Photolibrary.com; 10 ©Cape Girardeau Convention and Visitors Bureau; 12 ©Photolibrary.com; 14 ©Alamy/Photolibrary.com

Printed in China

ISBN 10: 0-15-350663-6
ISBN 13: 978-0-15-350663-5

Ordering Options
ISBN 10: 0-15-350599-0 (Grade 2 On-Level Collection)
ISBN 13: 978-0-15-350599-7 (Grade 2 On-Level Collection)
ISBN 10: 0-15-357844-0 (package of 5)
ISBN 13: 978-0-15-357844-1 (package of 5)

4 5 6 7 8 9 10   985   15 14 13 12 11 10 09 08

Characters

 Mom

 Jack

 Alex

 Aunt Sue

 Lisa

 Kim

SCENE ONE

Setting: Aunt Sue's house in Texas City, Texas

Jack: Hello, Aunt Sue. Are you and the girls just about ready to go?

Aunt Sue: Yes, we have been ready for hours! We have been waiting for you.

Mom: Let's get going without further delay!

Alex: There is so much to see and do. We don't have a minute to spare!

Aunt Sue: Come on, Lisa and Kim.

Lisa and Kim: We're coming!

Jack: Look out, Wisconsin! Here we come!

Setting: Harrison County Historical Museum in Marshall, Texas

Aunt Sue: The collection of historical items here is very impressive.

Lisa: Look at this grand ball gown.

Mom: Lady Bird Johnson wore this dress to a ball with her husband, President Johnson. Did you know she went to school here in Marshall?

Alex: Look in here, everyone. You can touch everything in this exhibit. These old toys are terrific.

Mom: It's time to leave now. We're off to our next stop, Arkansas.

Lisa and Kim: Oh, but this museum is so much fun. We haven't seen everything!

Jack: There's lots to do in Arkansas, and it will be lots of fun, too. Come on!

Setting: Riverfront Park in Little Rock, Arkansas

Kim: This zoo is really great.

Alex: The lions and tigers were awesome. They have huge, sharp claws.

Lisa: I liked the Petting Zoo, especially the goats.

Aunt Sue: This is a lovely park. It's wonderful here in the sunshine.

Jack: Look at the riverboat floating gently on the water.

Mom: Did you know that Little Rock was actually named after a small rock? Many settlers crossed the Mississippi River here.

Aunt Sue: We should go on a riverboat.

All the children: Can we, please?

Setting: Missouri Wall of Fame in Cape Girardeau, Missouri

Aunt Sue: This is a fantastic wall.

Mom: It's a flood wall. In a flood, the river water can't go beyond the wall and into the town.

Jack: It's common for the Mississippi River to flood.

Alex: Pictures of famous people from Missouri are painted on this wall.

Kim: Let's look on the other side of the wall.

Lisa: The painting on this side tells the history of Cape Girardeau. It starts here with the Native Americans who settled here long ago.

Jack: It finishes way down here with this bridge.

Aunt Sue: We are going to drive over that bridge tomorrow.

SCENE FIVE

Setting: Starved Rock State Park in Utica, Illinois

Kim: It's been fun camping here.

Jack: I'm feeling very upbeat. Let's going hiking in the canyons today!

Aunt Sue: Good idea!

Mom: The redbud trees are beautiful, but their flowers are not fragrant.

Alex: Look at that majestic waterfall.

Lisa: I hope I see a wood duck. That would be a rare discovery.

Aunt Sue: It's a long hike. Make sure you have some water and put on sunscreen.

SCENE 6

Setting: Lake Michigan in Milwaukee, Wisconsin

Mom: Well, here we are at Lake Michigan in Milwaukee.

Aunt Sue: Lake Michigan is one of the five Great Lakes. Michigan is across the lake from Milwaukee.

Jack: This entire trip has been fantastic.

Alex: Let's go and explore some more!

Lisa: I'd like to go on a paddleboat.

Kim: I'd like to go for a bike ride along the lake.

Aunt Sue: We have plenty of time for everything!

All the children: Hooray!

Think Critically

1. List in order the places where the family went.

2. What happens to the river water in Cape Girardeau when the Mississippi River floods?

3. Why do you think Aunt Sue told everyone to take water on the hike?

4. What words did the author use to make you know that the family had a good time in Texas?

5. Which place in the story would you like to visit? Why?

 **Social Studies**

Make a Brochure Make a brochure of places in your community that people might like to visit when they are on vacation.

School-Home Connection Tell family members about the story. Then talk about an interesting place you have visited on vacation.